MUSIC MAKERS

Contents

Haydn Middleton

Story illustrated by
Dan Chernett

Before Reading

In this story

Josh

Josh's mum

The judges

Tricky words

- practised
- natural
- guitar
- contestants
- audience
- nervous
- despair
- pleaded

Introduce these tricky words and help the reader when they come across them later!

Story starter

Josh likes playing his guitar and he is pretty good at it. But he doesn't practise much because he spends too much of his time watching TV. One day Josh was watching *Make or Break* – a TV talent contest to find the best young musicians.

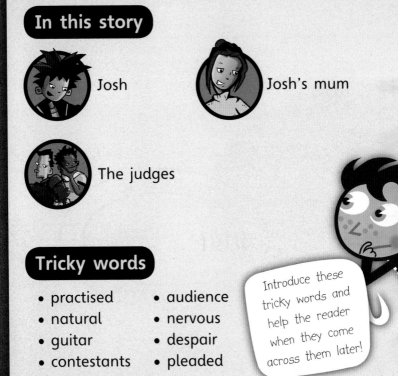

Make or Break

"This band is so bad," said Josh. "I could do much better."

"You could do much better if you practised more," said his mum.

"I don't need to practise," said Josh with a yawn. "I've got natural talent."

"*Everyone* needs to practise," said his mum.

Josh blinked. The TV seemed to be coming closer. He blinked again. No, he was getting closer to the TV. He was being sucked towards the screen!

"Mum!" he called, "help ..."

But it was too late – he was sucked right inside the TV.

Josh found himself in a strange room.

He still had his guitar in his hands.

All around him there were other people waiting. Josh realised he was backstage at *Make or Break* – and **he** was going to be one of the contestants!

"Cool," Josh thought, but his legs were trembling just a bit.

"**Next!**" called the judges. Josh watched a girl band go out on stage. They had to play their song to a live audience.
If the judges liked them, the girls might get to make a real CD which would be in all the shops.

But if the judges didn't like them, they might break the girls' hearts by saying nasty things about them. One judge was *really* harsh.

The girls started their song, but Josh could see they were all nervous and hitting the wrong notes.

When the girls had finished, not one judge said anything nice.

"That was absolutely awful," said the harsh judge. "You can't sing in tune and you can't play in tune. You will *never* make it in the pop world."

The next contestant was Josh.

"I've got natural talent," he told himself over and over. But then he realised he didn't have his plastic pick for plucking his guitar strings. He started plucking the strings with his fingers, and it sounded OK. "Hey," thought Josh, "I *am* going to be a star!"

Then Josh tried to sing too. But without his pick his fingers felt as clumsy as a bunch of bananas. He hit one wrong string, then another. The wrong notes made him sing out of tune.

The judges shook their heads.

The harsh judge closed his eyes in despair.

Josh wished the stage would open up and swallow him. People in the audience were laughing and booing.

Josh was making such a mess of the song that he stopped playing altogether.

"Look," he pleaded with the judges, "I don't always sound like this ..."

"I should hope you don't!" said the harsh judge.

"If someone could just lend me a pick," said Josh, "I'm sure I'd play much better."

But the harsh judge shook his head.

"I don't believe you," he said. "*Next!*"

"No, wait a minute," said another judge.
"Does anyone backstage have a guitar
pick they can lend this guy?"
A boy came up to Josh.
"Have this," he said, giving Josh his pick.
"Hey, thanks," said Josh. "Thanks a lot!"

What do you think will happen now?

Josh started his song again, using the pick. There was no problem now.

He was hitting every single string just right. No more banana fingers!

The audience began to nod their heads in time to the music. Josh strutted around like a rock guitarist. YESSS!

"Hmm," said the nicest judge when Josh had finished. "That wasn't too bad, but you *did* sound out of practice."

"Out of practice!" snorted the harsh judge. "Out of touch, out of tune and completely out of order!"

Then ... *ZAP!* It all went dark.

Josh found himself back on his sofa.

"I turned the TV off," said his mum. "You were fast asleep."

"Did I dream it?" thought Josh.

But then he felt something in his hand. It was the pick the boy had given him! Josh took his guitar and started playing his song again.

"If you practise," said his mum, "then one day you could be on TV too!"

Quiz

Text Detective

- Why did Josh hit the wrong strings on his guitar?
- Do you think Josh will practise more now? Why?

Word Detective

- Phonic Focus: Identifying phonemes in complex words
  Page 5: How many syllables are there in 'waiting'?
  What is the vowel phoneme in each syllable?
- Page 10: What are Josh's fingers compared to?
- Page 11: Find a word that means 'begged'.

Super Speller

Read these words:

towards another finished

Now try to spell them!

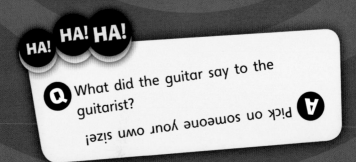

HA! HA! HA!

Q What did the guitar say to the guitarist?

A Pick on someone your own size!

17

Find out about

• Famous people who play the guitar

Tricky words

• guitar
• practised
• tortoises
• musicians
• mysterious
• remembered
• cinema

Introduce these tricky words and help the reader when they come across them later!

Text starter

You can play all sorts of music on a guitar. Many guitarists use a pick to pluck the strings. These picks used to be made from tortoise shells. Famous guitarists play so well because they practise all the time. Read on to learn about famous guitarists like Django Reinhardt and Bill Haley.

Famous Guitarists

You can play all sorts of music on a guitar.
How many of these sorts do you know?

- Rock
- Pop
- Jazz
- Blues
- Soul
- Folk
- Reggae
- Country
- Classical

How do famous guitarists play so well?

- Some guitarists used to use tortoises to help them play!
- One blues guitarist was said to have been helped by magic!
- One rock guitarist practised so much, he even took his guitar into the toilet!

To find out what is behind these stories, read on ...

Tortoise blues!

Many guitarists use a pick to pluck their guitar strings. Today picks are usually made of plastic.

But guess what?

Picks used to be made from tortoise shells!

Like magic?

In the 1930s Robert Johnson wanted to be a great blues guitarist. But he played so badly that other musicians laughed at him. Robert went away for a year. When he came back he could play the guitar so well it was spooky! How did he get so good?

There were many legends about a ghostly man you could meet at a crossroads at midnight. This man could tune your guitar so you could play like magic.

Robert later wrote a song called *Crossroads Blues*. Had he gone to see this mysterious person?

The Rolling Stones and the White Stripes have recorded songs by Robert Johnson.

Handy horror!

Django Reinhardt was a brilliant jazz guitarist.

When he was 18 there was a fire in his home. Django was so badly burned he nearly died, and afterwards he couldn't use two fingers on his left hand. But he *still* became a world famous jazz guitarist.

Many years later, Tony Iommi lost the tips of two fingers working in a factory. Tony had dreamed of being a rock guitarist, and he remembered how Django had played on after his accident. So Tony played on too, and became a famous rock guitarist in the band Black Sabbath.

Cool or what?

Music fans think guitar players look very cool.

At rock concerts the fans go crazy for guitarists in bands and solo guitarists. At home they put up posters of these famous players on their bedroom walls.

But do you think **this** guy looks cool?

Fifty years ago music fans thought he was really cool!

His name was Bill Haley and with his band he made one of the first great rock and roll records, *Rock Around the Clock*.

Even when fans watched films of Bill playing and singing, they went so crazy they smashed up seats in the cinema!

Teeth and ears!

Jimi Hendrix was a rock and blues guitarist. He loved his guitar so much he practised nearly all the time – he even took his guitar into the toilet with him!

Jimi did all sorts of tricks with his guitar on stage. He played it behind his back, and he could even play it with his teeth!

Pete Townshend is a famous guitarist
in a rock band called The Who.
He could play his guitar in mid-air.
Sometimes Pete played his guitars so
hard on stage that he broke them!
But the guitars got their revenge.
Because Pete played them so loudly,
he began to go deaf!

Starting out

About fifty years ago some school friends formed a band in Liverpool. They became the most famous musicians in the world: The Beatles. Maybe you could form a band of your own at school and become as famous as The Beatles!

Jimi Hendrix got his first guitar when he was 14 years old.

People all over the world start learning to play the guitar when they are young. Then the really great guitarists never stop learning.

You could be the next great guitar hero, but remember:

You must keep practising!

Quiz

Text Detective

- What used to be made from tortoise shells?
- Would you like to be a famous musician? Why or why not?

Word Detective

- **Phonic Focus:** Identifying phonemes in complex words
  Page 20: How many syllables are there in 'behind'?
  What is the vowel phoneme in each syllable?
- Page 26: What does the word 'solo' mean?
- Page 27: Why are the words 'Rock Around the Clock' in italics?

Super Speller

Read these words:

famous   usually   loudly

Now try to spell them!

HA! HA! HA!

Q What's the difference between a guitar and a tuna fish?

A You can tune a guitar but you can't tuna fish!